Make Gratitude your new habit

As you practice your new habit each day

Commend your advancement and mark off every day of your endeavors

D1542182

this planner belongs to

_____

_____

if you want to change the world,
start off by making your bed.

Date: __/__/__

MY monthly plans:

> '*If you do not change direction,*
> *you may end up where you are*'
> Lao Tzu

Goals I envision:

_____

_____

_____

Improvements I seek:

_____

_____

_____

Notes:

_____

_____

_____

Date: __/__/__

Today, I am grateful for:

_____
_____
_____

How will I make today awesome?

_____
_____
_____

Positive affirmations:

_____
_____
_____

Choosing to be positive and having a grateful attitude is going to determine how you're going to live your life.

Joel Osteen

today's amazing moments:

_____
_____
_____

How could I have made this day even better?

_____
_____
_____

Goals/Plans for Tomorrow:

_____   *I am feel*
_____   ☺ ☺ ☺ ☺

Date: __/__/__

Today, I am grateful for:

_____
_____
_____

How will I make today awesome?

_____
_____
_____

Positive affirmations:

_____
_____
_____

Only the wisest and stupidest of men never change.
Confucius

today's amazing moments:

_____
_____
_____

How could I have made this day even better?

_____
_____
_____

Goals/Plans for Tomorrow:

_____   *I am feel*
_____   ☺ ☺ ☺ ☺

Date: __/__/__

Today, I am grateful for:

_____
_____
_____

How will I make today awesome?

_____
_____
_____

Positive affirmations:

_____
_____
_____

Change in all things is sweet

Aristotle

today's amazing moments:

_____
_____
_____

How could I have made this day even better?

_____
_____
_____

Goals/Plans for Tomorrow:

_____   *I am feel*

_____   😄 😊 😐 😒

Date: __/__/__

Today, I am grateful for:

_____
_____
_____

How will I make today awesome?

_____
_____
_____

Positive affirmations:

_____
_____
_____

For success, attitude is equally as important as ability.

Walter Scott

today's amazing moments:

_____
_____
_____

How could I have made this day even better?

_____
_____
_____

Goals/Plans for Tomorrow:

_____   *I am feel*

_____   😀 😊 😐 😒

Date: __/__/__

Today, I am grateful for:

_____

_____

_____

How will I make today awesome?

_____

_____

_____

Positive affirmations:

_____

_____

_____

If you get a diagnosis, get on a therapy, keep a good attitude and keep your sense of humor

Teri Garr

today's amazing moments:

_____

_____

_____

How could I have made this day even better?

_____

_____

_____

Goals/Plans for Tomorrow:

I am feel

_____   😀 😊 😐 😒

_____

Date: __/__/__

Today, I am grateful for:

_____

_____

_____

How will I make today awesome?

_____

_____

_____

Positive affirmations:

_____

_____

_____

Change your opinions, keep to your principles ;
change your leaves, keep intact your roots

Victor Hugo

today's amazing moments:

_____

_____

_____

How could I have made this day even better?

_____

_____

_____

Goals/Plans for Tomorrow:

I am feel

_____

😀 😊 😐 😑

_____

Date: __/__/__

Today, I am grateful for:

_____
_____
_____

How will I make today awesome?

_____
_____
_____

Positive affirmations:

_____
_____
_____

It is in the character of very few men to honor without envy a friend who has prospered.

Aeschylus

today's amazing moments:

_____
_____
_____

How could I have made this day even better?

_____
_____
_____

Goals/Plans for Tomorrow:

_____   *I am feel*

_____   ☺ ☺ ☺ ☺

Date: __/__/__

Today, I am grateful for:

_____
_____
_____

How will I make today awesome?

_____
_____
_____

Positive affirmations:

_____
_____
_____

The ideal attitude is to be physically loose and mentally tight.

Arthur Ashe

today's amazing moments:

_____
_____
_____

How could I have made this day even better?

_____
_____
_____

Goals/Plans for Tomorrow:

_____

I am feel

😀 😊 😐 😑

Date: __/__/__

Today, I am grateful for:

_____
_____

_____

How will I make today awesome?

_____
_____

_____

Positive affirmations:

_____
_____

_____

Reject your sense of injury and the injury itself disappears.

Marcus Aurelius

today's amazing moments:

_____
_____

_____

How could I have made this day even better?

_____
_____

_____

Goals/Plans for Tomorrow:

_____

_____

I am feel

☺ ☺ ☺ ☺

Date: __/__/__

Today,I am grateful for:

_____
_____
_____

How will I make today awesome?

_____
_____
_____

Positive affirmations:

_____
_____
_____

Attitude is a little thing that makes a big difference
Winston Churchill

today's amazing moments:

_____
_____
_____

How could I have made this day even better?

_____
_____
_____

Goals/Plans for Tomorrow:

I am feel

_____   😃 😊 🙂 😐

Date: __/__/__

Today, I am grateful for:

_____
_____
_____

How will I make today awesome?

_____
_____
_____

Positive affirmations:

_____
_____
_____

The reactionary is always willing to take a progressive attitude on any issue that is dead

Theodore Roosevelt

today's amazing moments:

_____
_____
_____

How could I have made this day even better?

_____
_____
_____

Goals/Plans for Tomorrow:

I am feel

_____   😄 😊 😐 😒
_____

Date: __/__/__

Today, I am grateful for:

_____
_____
_____

How will I make today awesome?

_____
_____
_____

Positive affirmations:

_____
_____

You cannot tailor-make the situations in life but you can tailor-make the attitudes to fit those situations.

Zig Ziglar

today's amazing moments:

_____
_____
_____

How could I have made this day even better?

_____
_____
_____

Goals/Plans for Tomorrow:

I am feel

_____

😃 😊 🙂 😐

Date: __/__/__

Today, I am grateful for:

_____
_____
_____

How will I make today awesome?

_____
_____
_____

Positive affirmations:

_____
_____
_____

Change your opinions, keep to your principles ;
change your leaves, keep intact your roots

Victor Hugo

today's amazing moments:

_____
_____
_____

How could I have made this day even better?

_____
_____
_____

Goals/Plans for Tomorrow:

_____   *I am feel*

_____   😀 😊 🙂 😑

Date: __/__/__

Today, I am grateful for:

_____
_____
_____

How will I make today awesome?

_____
_____
_____

Positive affirmations:

_____
_____
_____

The remarkable thing is, we have a choice everyday regarding the attitude we will embrace for that day
                                        Charles R. Swindoll

today's amazing moments:

_____
_____
_____

How could I have made this day even better?

_____
_____
_____

Goals/Plans for Tomorrow:

_____   *I am feel*

_____   😃 😊 😐 😕

Date: __/__/__

Today, I am grateful for:

_____

_____

_____

How will I make today awesome?

_____

_____

_____

Positive affirmations:

_____

_____

_____

Take the attitude of a student, never be too big to ask questions, never know too much to learn something new.

Og Mandino

today's amazing moments:

_____

_____

_____

How could I have made this day even better?

_____

_____

_____

Goals/Plans for Tomorrow:

I am feel

_____   ☺ ☺ ☺ ☺

Date: __/__/__

Today, I am grateful for:

_____
_____
_____

How will I make today awesome?

_____
_____
_____

Positive affirmations:

_____
_____
_____

Individuals need to be willing to face truth about their attitudes, behaviors, even what we want out of life·
                                                    Joyce Meyer

today's amazing moments:

_____
_____
_____

How could I have made this day even better?

_____
_____
_____

Goals/Plans for Tomorrow: I am feel

_____   ☺ ☺ ☺ ☺
_____

Date: __/__/__

Today, I am grateful for:

_____
_____
_____

How will I make today awesome?

_____
_____
_____

Positive affirmations:

_____
_____
_____

Change in all things is sweet

Aristotle

today's amazing moments:

_____
_____
_____

How could I have made this day even better?

_____
_____
_____

Goals/Plans for Tomorrow:

_____

I am feel

☺ ☺ ☺ ☺

Today,I am grateful for:

_____
_____
_____

How will I make today awesome?

_____
_____
_____

Positive affirmations:

_____
_____
_____

Only the wisest and stupidest of men never change

confucius

today's amazing moments:

_____
_____
_____

How could I have made this day even better?

_____
_____
_____

Goals/Plans for Tomorrow:

I am feel

_____   ☺ ☺ ☺ ☺
_____

Date: __/__/__

Today, I am grateful for:

_____
_____
_____

How will I make today awesome?

_____
_____
_____

Positive affirmations:

_____
_____
_____

Things do not change; we change.

Henry David Thoreau

today's amazing moments:

_____
_____
_____

How could I have made this day even better?

_____
_____
_____

Goals/Plans for Tomorrow:

I am feel

_____   ☺ ☺ ☺ ☺

Date: __/__/__

Today, I am grateful for:

_____
_____
_____

How will I make today awesome?

_____
_____
_____

Positive affirmations:

_____
_____

I'm sick of following my dreams· I'm just going to ask them where they're goin', and hook up with them later·

Mitch Hedberg

today's amazing moments:

_____
_____
_____

How could I have made this day even better?

_____
_____
_____

Goals/Plans for Tomorrow:

_____   *I am feel*

_____   😀 😊 😐 😒

Date: __/__/__

Today, I am grateful for:

_____
_____
_____

How will I make today awesome?

_____
_____
_____

Positive affirmations:

_____
_____
_____

You have to dream before your dreams can come true.

Abdul Kalam

today's amazing moments:

_____
_____
_____

How could I have made this day even better?

_____
_____
_____

Goals/Plans for Tomorrow:

I am feel

_____
_____

😃 😊 😐 😑

Date: __/__/__

Today, I am grateful for:

_____
_____

_____

How will I make today awesome?

_____
_____

_____

Positive affirmations:

_____
_____

_____

Hold fast to dreams For when dreams go Life is a barren field Frozen with snow

Langston Hughes

today's amazing moments:

_____
_____

_____

How could I have made this day even better?

_____
_____

_____

Goals/Plans for Tomorrow:

_____   *I am feel*

_____   😃 😊 😐 😑

Date: __/__/__

Today, I am grateful for:

_____
_____
_____

How will I make today awesome?

_____
_____
_____

Positive affirmations:

_____
_____
_____

The most pitiful among men is he who turns his dreams into silver and gold.

Khalil Gibran

today's amazing moments:

_____
_____
_____

How could I have made this day even better?

_____
_____
_____

Goals/Plans for Tomorrow:

I am feel

_____   😃 😊 😐 😒
_____

Date: __/__/__

Today, I am grateful for:

_____
_____
_____

How will I make today awesome?

_____
_____
_____

Positive affirmations:

_____
_____
_____

I am indeed amazed when I consider how weak my mind is and how prone to error.

Rene Descartes

today's amazing moments:

_____
_____
_____

How could I have made this day even better?

_____
_____
_____

Goals/Plans for Tomorrow:

_____

I am feel

☺ ☺ ☺ ☺

Date: __/__/__

Today, I am grateful for:

_____
_____
_____

How will I make today awesome?

_____
_____
_____

Positive affirmations:

_____
_____
_____

With love, you should go ahead and take the risk of getting hurt because love is an amazing feeling.

Britney Spears

today's amazing moments:

_____
_____
_____

How could I have made this day even better?

_____
_____
_____

Goals/Plans for Tomorrow:

I am feel

_____   😃 😊 🙂 😐

_____

Date: __/__/__

Today,I am grateful for:

_____
_____

_____

How will I make today awesome?

_____
_____

_____

Positive affirmations:

_____
_____

_____

I'm not a kid anymore. And I'm excited for all the amazing things to come

Paris Hilton

today's amazing moments:

_____
_____

_____

How could I have made this day even better?

_____
_____

_____

Goals/Plans for Tomorrow:

I am feel

_____   😃 😊 😐 😒
_____

Date: __/__/__

Today,I am grateful for:

_____
_____
_____

How will I make today awesome?

_____
_____
_____

Positive affirmations:

_____
_____
_____

I have never taken any exercise, except sleeping and resting, and I never intend to take any.

Mark Twain

today's amazing moments:

_____
_____
_____

How could I have made this day even better?

_____
_____
_____

Goals/Plans for Tomorrow:

I am feel

_____   ☺ ☺ ☺ ☹
_____

Date: __/__/__

Today, I am grateful for:

_____
_____
_____

How will I make today awesome?

_____
_____
_____

Positive affirmations:

_____
_____
_____

You cannot escape the responsibility of tomorrow by evading it today.

Abraham Lincoln

today's amazing moments:

_____
_____
_____

How could I have made this day even better?

_____
_____
_____

Goals/Plans for Tomorrow:

_____   I am feel

_____   :D :) :o :-|

Date: __/__/__

Today, I am grateful for:

_____

_____

_____

How will I make today awesome?

_____

_____

_____

Positive affirmations:

_____

_____

Never let the future disturb you. You will meet it, if you have to, with the same weapons of reason which today arm you against the present.

Marcus Aurelius

today's amazing moments:

_____

_____

_____

How could I have made this day even better?

_____

_____

_____

Goals/Plans for Tomorrow:

_____

_____

I am feel

☺ ☺ ☺ ☺

Date: __/__/__

Today, I am grateful for:

_____
_____

_____

How will I make today awesome?

_____
_____

_____

Positive affirmations:

_____
_____

_____

I never think of the future - it comes soon enough.

Albert Einstein

today's amazing moments:

_____
_____

_____

How could I have made this day even better?

_____
_____

_____

Goals/Plans for Tomorrow:

I am feel

_____

☺ ☺ ☺ ☺

Date: __/__/__

Today, I am grateful for:

_____
_____
_____

How will I make today awesome?

_____
_____
_____

Positive affirmations:

_____
_____
_____

The future influences the present just as much as the past ·

Friedrich Nietzsche

today's amazing moments:

_____
_____
_____

How could I have made this day even better?

_____
_____
_____

Goals/Plans for Tomorrow:

_____

I am feel

☺ ☺ ☺ ☺

Date: __/__/__

Today, I am grateful for:

_____

_____

_____

How will I make today awesome?

_____

_____

_____

Positive affirmations:

_____

_____

_____

Happiness is when what you think, what you say,
and what you do are in harmony

Mahatma Gandhi

today's amazing moments:

_____

_____

_____

How could I have made this day even better?

_____

_____

_____

Goals/Plans for Tomorrow:

I am feel

_____   😃 😊 😐 😒

_____

Date: __/__/__

Today, I am grateful for:
_____
_____
_____

How will I make today awesome?
_____
_____
_____

Positive affirmations:
_____
_____
_____

If you want others to be happy, practice compassion.
If you want to be happy, practice compassion.

Dalai Lama

today's amazing moments:
_____
_____
_____

How could I have made this day even better?
_____
_____
_____

Goals/Plans for Tomorrow: *I am feel*
_____   ☺ ☺ ☺ ☺
_____

Date: __/__/__

Today, I am grateful for:

_____
_____
_____

How will I make today awesome?

_____
_____
_____

Positive affirmations:

_____
_____
_____

Everything has its wonders, even darkness and silence, and I learn, whatever state I may be in, therein to be content   *Helen Keller*

today's amazing moments:

_____
_____
_____

How could I have made this day even better?

_____
_____
_____

Goals/Plans for Tomorrow: *I am feel*

_____   😃 😊 😐 😒
_____

Date: __/__/__

Today, I am grateful for:

_____
_____

_____

How will I make today awesome?

_____
_____

_____

Positive affirmations:

_____

_____

_____

You can't get a cup of tea big enough or a book long enough to suit me.

C. S. Lewis

today's amazing moments:

_____
_____

_____

How could I have made this day even better?

_____
_____

_____

Goals/Plans for Tomorrow:

_____   *I am feel*

_____   ☺ ☺ ☺ ☹

Date: __/__/__

Today, I am grateful for:

_____
_____
_____

How will I make today awesome?

_____
_____
_____

Positive affirmations:

_____
_____
_____

It is neither wealth nor splendor; but tranquility and occupation which give you

Thomas Mann

today's amazing moments:

_____
_____
_____

How could I have made this day even better?

_____
_____
_____

Goals/Plans for Tomorrow:

I am feel

_____   ☺ ☺ ☺ ☺
_____

Date: __/__/__

Today, I am grateful for:

_____

_____

_____

How will I make today awesome?

_____

_____

_____

Positive affirmations:

_____

_____

_____

Your successes and happiness are forgiven you only if you generously consent to share them.

                                    Albert Camus

today's amazing moments:

_____

_____

_____

How could I have made this day even better?

_____

_____

_____

Goals/Plans for Tomorrow:

                              I am feel

_____   😃 😌 😐 😕

_____

Date: __/__/__

Today, I am grateful for:

_____
_____

_____

How will I make today awesome?

_____
_____

_____

Positive affirmations:

_____
_____

_____

A happy life must be to a great extent a quiet life,
for it is only in an atmosphere of quiet that true
joy dare live.   Bertrand Russell

today's amazing moments:

_____
_____

_____

How could I have made this day even better?

_____
_____

_____

Goals/Plans for Tomorrow:

                                        I am feel
_____
                                    ☺ ☺ ☺ ☺
_____

Date: __/__/__

Today, I am grateful for:

_____
_____
_____

How will I make today awesome?

_____
_____
_____

Positive affirmations:

_____
_____
_____

It is in the compelling zest of high adventure and of victory, and in creative action, that man finds his supreme joys.   Antoine de Saint-Exupery

today's amazing moments:

_____
_____
_____

How could I have made this day even better?

_____
_____
_____

Goals/Plans for Tomorrow: *I am feel*

_____   😀 😊 😐 😕
_____

Date: __/__/__

Today, I am grateful for:

_____
_____
_____

How will I make today awesome?

_____
_____
_____

Positive affirmations:

_____
_____
_____

There is something curiously boring about somebody else's happiness ·

Aldous Huxley

today's amazing moments:

_____
_____
_____

How could I have made this day even better?

_____
_____
_____

Goals/Plans for Tomorrow:

_____   *I am feel*

_____   😃 😊 😐 😒

Date: __/__/__

Today, I am grateful for:

_____
_____

_____

How will I make today awesome?

_____
_____

_____

Positive affirmations:

_____
_____

_____

Action may not always bring happiness; but there is no happiness without action .

Benjamin Disraeli

today's amazing moments:

_____
_____

_____

How could I have made this day even better?

_____
_____

_____

Goals/Plans for Tomorrow:

I am feel

_____
_____

😀 😌 😐 😒

Date: __/__/__

Today, I am grateful for:

_____
_____

_____

How will I make today awesome?

_____
_____

_____

Positive affirmations:

_____
_____

_____

All who joy would win must share it. Happiness was born a Twin.

Lord Byron

today's amazing moments:

_____
_____

_____

How could I have made this day even better?

_____
_____

_____

Goals/Plans for Tomorrow:

I am feel

_____   😃 😊 😐 😒

_____

Date: __/__/__

Today, I am grateful for:

_____
_____
_____

How will I make today awesome?

_____
_____
_____

Positive affirmations:

_____
_____
_____

The best way to pay for a lovely moment is to enjoy it.

Richard Bach

today's amazing moments:

_____
_____
_____

How could I have made this day even better?

_____
_____
_____

Goals/Plans for Tomorrow:

I am feel

_____

😃 😊 😐 😒

Date: __/__/__

Today,I am grateful for:

_____
_____

_____

How will I make today awesome?

_____
_____

_____

Positive affirmations:

_____
_____

_____

Remember that the happiest people are not those getting more, but those giving more.

Jackson Browne

today's amazing moments:

_____
_____

_____

How could I have made this day even better?

_____
_____

_____

Goals/Plans for Tomorrow:

_____   *I am feel*

_____   😃 😊 😐 😒

Date: __/__/__

Today, I am grateful for:

_____

_____

_____

How will I make today awesome?

_____

_____

_____

Positive affirmations:

_____

_____

_____

The word 'Islam' means 'peace.' The word 'Muslim' means 'one who surrenders to God.' But the press makes us seem like haters.

Muhammad Ali

today's amazing moments:

_____

_____

_____

How could I have made this day even better?

_____

_____

_____

Goals/Plans for Tomorrow:

I am feel

_____

_____

😃 😊 😐 😑

Date: __/__/__

Today, I am grateful for:

_____
_____
_____

How will I make today awesome?

_____
_____
_____

Positive affirmations:

_____
_____
_____

Optimism is the faith that leads to achievement.
Nothing can be done without hope and confidence.

Helen Keller

today's amazing moments:

_____
_____
_____

How could I have made this day even better?

_____
_____
_____

Goals/Plans for Tomorrow:

_____   *I am feel*

_____   😃 😊 😐 😒

Date: __/__/__

Today, I am grateful for:
_____
_____
_____

How will I make today awesome?
_____
_____
_____

Positive affirmations:
_____
_____
_____

Well done is better than well said.

Benjamin Franklin

today's amazing moments:
_____
_____
_____

How could I have made this day even better?
_____
_____
_____

Goals/Plans for Tomorrow:

I am feel
_____
😀 😊 🙂 😑

Date: __/__/__

Today, I am grateful for:

_____
_____
_____

How will I make today awesome?

_____
_____
_____

Positive affirmations:

_____
_____
_____

Good, better, best. Never let it rest. 'Til your good is better and your better is best

St. Jerome

today's amazing moments:

_____
_____
_____

How could I have made this day even better?

_____
_____
_____

Goals/Plans for Tomorrow:

I am feel

_____
😃 😊 😐 😖

Date: __/__/__

Today, I am grateful for:

_____
_____
_____

How will I make today awesome?

_____
_____
_____

Positive affirmations:

_____
_____
_____

Knowing is not enough; we must apply. Willing is not enough; we must do.

Johann Wolfgang von Goethe

today's amazing moments:

_____
_____
_____

How could I have made this day even better?

_____
_____
_____

Goals/Plans for Tomorrow:

_____
_____

I am feel

😀 😊 😐 😣

Date: __/__/__

Today, I am grateful for:

_____
_____
_____

How will I make today awesome?

_____
_____
_____

Positive affirmations:

_____
_____

I know where I'm going and I know the truth, and
I don't have to be what you want me to be.
I'm free to be what I want

Muhammad Ali

today's amazing moments:

_____
_____
_____

How could I have made this day even better?

_____
_____
_____

Goals/Plans for Tomorrow:

I am feel

_____   ☺ ☺ ☺ ☺

Date: __/__/__

Today, I am grateful for:

_____
_____

_____

How will I make today awesome?

_____
_____

_____

Positive affirmations:

_____
_____

_____

Failure will never overtake me if my determination to succeed is strong enough.

Og Mandino

today's amazing moments:

_____
_____

_____

How could I have made this day even better?

_____
_____

_____

Goals/Plans for Tomorrow:

I am feel

_____

☺ ☺ ☺ ☺

_____

Date: __/__/__

Today, I am grateful for:

_____
_____
_____

How will I make today awesome?

_____
_____
_____

Positive affirmations:

_____
_____
_____

Be miserable. Or motivate yourself. Whatever has to be done, it's always your choice.

                                        VWayne Dyer

today's amazing moments:

_____
_____
_____

How could I have made this day even better?

_____
_____
_____

Goals/Plans for Tomorrow: *I am feel*

_____   ☺ ☺ ☺ ☺
_____

Date: __/__/__

Today, I am grateful for:

_____
_____
_____

How will I make today awesome?

_____
_____
_____

Positive affirmations:

_____
_____
_____

Motivation is the art of getting people to do what you want them to do because they want to do it.
                                    Dwight D. Eisenhower

today's amazing moments:

_____
_____
_____

How could I have made this day even better?

_____
_____
_____

Goals/Plans for Tomorrow: *I am feel*

_____   ☺ ☺ ☺ ☹
_____

Date: __/__/__

Today, I am grateful for:

_____

_____

_____

How will I make today awesome?

_____

_____

_____

Positive affirmations:

_____

_____

_____

If you don't like how things are, change it!
You're not a tree.

Jim Rohn

today's amazing moments:

_____

_____

_____

How could I have made this day even better?

_____

_____

_____

Goals/Plans for Tomorrow:

_____   *I am feel*

_____   ☺ ☺ ☺ ☺

Date: __/__/__

Today, I am grateful for:

_____
_____
_____

How will I make today awesome?

_____
_____
_____

Positive affirmations:

_____
_____
_____

No bird soars too high if he soars with his own wings·
William Blake

today's amazing moments:

_____
_____
_____

How could I have made this day even better?

_____
_____
_____

Goals/Plans for Tomorrow:

_____   *I am feel*
_____   ☺ ☺ ☺ ☹

Date: __/__/__

Today,I am grateful for:
_____
_____
_____

How will I make today awesome?
_____
_____
_____

Positive affirmations:
_____
_____
_____

Setting goals is the first step in turning the invisible into the visible.

Tony Robbins

today's amazing moments:
_____
_____
_____

How could I have made this day even better?
_____
_____
_____

Goals/Plans for Tomorrow:

I am feel

_____   😃 😊 😐 😒

_____

Date: __/__/__

Today, I am grateful for:

_____
_____
_____

How will I make today awesome?

_____
_____
_____

Positive affirmations:

_____
_____
_____

The will to succeed is important, but what's more important is the will to prepare.

Bobby Knight

today's amazing moments:

_____
_____
_____

How could I have made this day even better?

_____
_____
_____

Goals/Plans for Tomorrow:

I am feel

_____
_____

Date: __/__/__

Today, I am grateful for:

_____
_____
_____

How will I make today awesome?

_____
_____
_____

Positive affirmations:

_____
_____
_____

If you don't ask, you don't get.

Stevie Wonder

today's amazing moments:

_____
_____
_____

How could I have made this day even better?

_____
_____
_____

Goals/Plans for Tomorrow:

I am feel

_____   ☺ ☺ ☺ ☺
_____

Date: __/__/__

Today, I am grateful for:

_____

_____

_____

How will I make today awesome?

_____

_____

_____

Positive affirmations:

_____

_____

_____

Without hard work, nothing grows but weeds.

Gordon B. Hinckley

today's amazing moments:

_____

_____

_____

How could I have made this day even better?

_____

_____

_____

Goals/Plans for Tomorrow:

I am feel

_____   😀 😊 😐 😕

_____

Date: __/__/__

Today, I am grateful for:

_____
_____
_____

How will I make today awesome?

_____
_____
_____

Positive affirmations:

_____
_____
_____

Don't give up. Don't lose hope. Don't sell out.
Christopher Reeve

today's amazing moments:

_____
_____
_____

How could I have made this day even better?

_____
_____
_____

Goals/Plans for Tomorrow:

_____   *I am feel*

_____   ☺ ☺ ☺ ☹

Date: __/__/__

Today, I am grateful for:

_____
_____
_____

How will I make today awesome?

_____
_____
_____

Positive affirmations:

_____
_____
_____

Never retreat. Never explain. Get it done and let them howl.

Benjamin Jowett

today's amazing moments:

_____
_____
_____

How could I have made this day even better?

_____
_____
_____

Goals/Plans for Tomorrow:

I am feel

_____
_____

😀 😊 😶 😒

Date: __/__/__

Today, I am grateful for:
_____
_____
_____

How will I make today awesome?
_____
_____
_____

Positive affirmations:
_____
_____
_____

You just can't beat the person who never gives up.
Babe Ruth

today's amazing moments:
_____
_____
_____

How could I have made this day even better?
_____
_____
_____

Goals/Plans for Tomorrow: *I am feel*
_____   ☺ ☺ ☺ ☺
_____

Date: __/__/__

Today, I am grateful for:

_____

_____

_____

How will I make today awesome?

_____

_____

_____

Positive affirmations:

_____

_____

_____

Perseverance is not a long race; it is many short races one after the other.

Walter Elliot

today's amazing moments:

_____

_____

_____

How could I have made this day even better?

_____

_____

_____

Goals/Plans for Tomorrow:

_____   *I am feel*

_____   😃 😊 😐 😕

Date: __/__/__

Today, I am grateful for:
_____
_____
_____

How will I make today awesome?
_____
_____
_____

Positive affirmations:
_____
_____
_____

Step by step and the thing is done.

Charles Atlas

today's amazing moments:
_____
_____
_____

How could I have made this day even better?
_____
_____
_____

Goals/Plans for Tomorrow:
_____   I am feel
_____   😀 😊 😐 😒

Date: __/__/__

Today, I am grateful for:

_____

_____

_____

How will I make today awesome?

_____

_____

_____

Positive affirmations:

_____

_____

_____

What you get by achieving your goals is not as important as what you become by achieving your goals.

Zig Ziglar

today's amazing moments:

_____

_____

_____

How could I have made this day even better?

_____

_____

_____

Goals/Plans for Tomorrow:

_____

_____

I am feel

☺ ☺ ☺ ☺

Date: __/__/__

Today, I am grateful for:
_____
_____
_____

How will I make today awesome?
_____
_____
_____

Positive affirmations:
_____
_____
_____

We may encounter many defeats but we must not be defeated.

Maya Angelou

today's amazing moments:
_____
_____
_____

How could I have made this day even better?
_____
_____
_____

Goals/Plans for Tomorrow:
_____   *I am feel*
_____   😃 😊 😐 😠

Date: __/__/__

Today, I am grateful for:

_____
_____
_____

How will I make today awesome?

_____
_____
_____

Positive affirmations:

_____
_____
_____

Always desire to learn something useful·

Sophocles

today's amazing moments:

_____
_____
_____

How could I have made this day even better?

_____
_____
_____

Goals/Plans for Tomorrow:

I am feel

_____   ☺ ☺ ☺ ☺
_____

Date: __/__/__

Today, I am grateful for:

_____
_____

_____

How will I make today awesome?

_____
_____

_____

Positive affirmations:

_____
_____

_____

Get action. Seize the moment. Man was never intended to become an oyster.

Theodore Roosevelt

today's amazing moments:

_____
_____

_____

How could I have made this day even better?

_____
_____

_____

Goals/Plans for Tomorrow:

I am feel

_____   ☺ ☺ ☺ ☺
_____

Date: __/__/__

Today,I am grateful for:

_____
_____

_____

How will I make today awesome?

_____
_____

_____

Positive affirmations:

_____
_____

_____

When you reach the end of your rope, tie a knot in it and hang on.

Franklin D. Roosevelt

today's amazing moments:

_____
_____

_____

How could I have made this day even better?

_____
_____

_____

Goals/Plans for Tomorrow:

I am feel

_____   ☺ ☺ ☺ ☺
_____

Date: __/__/__

Today, I am grateful for:

_____
_____
_____

How will I make today awesome?

_____
_____
_____

Positive affirmations:

_____
_____
_____

Go for it now. The future is promised to no one.
Wayne Dyer

today's amazing moments: ·

_____
_____
_____

How could I have made this day even better?

_____
_____
_____

Goals/Plans for Tomorrow:

_____   *I am feel*

_____   ☺ ☺ ☺ ☺

Date: __/__/__

Today, I am grateful for:

_____
_____

_____

How will I make today awesome?

_____
_____

_____

Positive affirmations:

_____
_____

_____

You can't build a reputation on what you are going to do.

Henry Ford

today's amazing moments:

_____
_____

_____

How could I have made this day even better?

_____
_____

_____

Goals/Plans for Tomorrow:

_____

_____

I am feel

☺ ☺ ☺ ☺

Date: __/__/__

Today, I am grateful for:

_____
_____
_____

How will I make today awesome?

_____
_____
_____

Positive affirmations:

_____
_____
_____

*Change your opinions, keep to your principles ;
change your leaves, keep intact your roots*

Victor Hugo

today's amazing moments:

_____
_____
_____

How could I have made this day even better?

_____
_____
_____

Goals/Plans for Tomorrow:

_____   *I am feel*

_____   ☺ ☺ ☺ ☺

Date: __/__/__

Today,I am grateful for:

_____
_____

_____

How will I make today awesome?

_____
_____

_____

Positive affirmations:

_____
_____

_____

It always seems impossible until it's done.

Nelson Mandela

today's amazing moments:

_____
_____

_____

How could I have made this day even better?

_____
_____

_____

Goals/Plans for Tomorrow:

I am feel

_____

☺ ☺ ☺ ☺

Date: __/__/__

Today, I am grateful for:

_____

_____

_____

How will I make today awesome?

_____

_____

_____

Positive affirmations:

_____

_____

_____

A creative man is motivated by the desire to achieve, not by the desire to beat others.

Ayn Rand

today's amazing moments:

_____

_____

_____

How could I have made this day even better?

_____

_____

_____

Goals/Plans for Tomorrow:

I am feel

_____   ☺ ☺ ☺ ☺

Date: __/__/__

Today, I am grateful for:

_____
_____
_____

How will I make today awesome?

_____
_____
_____

Positive affirmations:

_____
_____
_____

When something is important enough, you do it even if the odds are not in your favor.

Elon Musk

today's amazing moments:

_____
_____
_____

How could I have made this day even better?

_____
_____
_____

Goals/Plans for Tomorrow:

I am feel

_____   ☺ ☺ ☺ ☺
_____

Date: __/__/__

Today, I am grateful for:

_____
_____

_____

How will I make today awesome?

_____
_____

_____

Positive affirmations:

_____
_____

_____

If you want to conquer fear, don't sit home and think about it. Go out and get busy.

Dale Carnegie

today's amazing moments:

_____
_____

_____

How could I have made this day even better?

_____
_____

_____

Goals/Plans for Tomorrow:

I am feel

_____   😀 😊 🙂 😑

_____

Date: __/__/__

Today, I am grateful for:

_____
_____
_____

How will I make today awesome?

_____
_____
_____

Positive affirmations:

_____
_____
_____

Be miserable. Or motivate yourself. Whatever has to be done, it's always your choice.

Wayne Dyer

today's amazing moments:

_____
_____
_____

How could I have made this day even better?

_____
_____
_____

Goals/Plans for Tomorrow:

I am feel

_____   ☺ ☺ ☺ ☺
_____

Date: __/__/__

Today, I am grateful for:

_____
_____

_____

How will I make today awesome?

_____
_____

_____

Positive affirmations:

_____
_____

_____

*Our greatest weakness lies in giving up. The most
certain way to succeed is always to try just one
more time.*
                                    Thomas A. Edison

today's amazing moments:

_____
_____

_____

How could I have made this day even better?

_____
_____

_____

Goals/Plans for Tomorrow:
                                    I am feel
_____
                              😃 😊 🙂 😕
_____

Date: __/__/__

Today, I am grateful for:

_____
_____
_____

How will I make today awesome?

_____
_____
_____

Positive affirmations:

_____
_____
_____

If you want to succeed you should strike out on new paths, rather than travel the worn paths of accepted success.   John D. Rockefeller

today's amazing moments:

_____
_____
_____

How could I have made this day even better?

_____
_____
_____

Goals/Plans for Tomorrow:

_____   *I am feel*

_____   ☺ ☺ ☺ ☺

Date: __/__/__

Today, I am grateful for:

_____
_____

_____

How will I make today awesome?

_____
_____

_____

Positive affirmations:

_____
_____

_____

The more things you do, the more you can do.

Lucille Ball

today's amazing moments:

_____
_____

_____

How could I have made this day even better?

_____
_____

_____

Goals/Plans for Tomorrow:

I am feel

_____   😃 😊 😐 😣
_____

Date: __/__/__

Today,I am grateful for:

_____
_____

_____

How will I make today awesome?

_____
_____

_____

Positive affirmations:

_____
_____

_____

Change your opinions, keep to your principles ;
change your leaves, keep intact your roots

Lucille Ball

today's amazing moments:

_____
_____

_____

How could I have made this day even better?

_____
_____

_____

Goals/Plans for Tomorrow:

I am feel

_____   ☺ ☺ ☺ ☺
_____

Date: __/__/__

Today, I am grateful for:

_____
_____

_____

How will I make today awesome?

_____
_____

_____

Positive affirmations:

_____
_____

_____

One may miss the mark by aiming too high as too low.

Thomas Fuller

today's amazing moments:

_____
_____

_____

How could I have made this day even better?

_____
_____

_____

Goals/Plans for Tomorrow:

_____

I am feel

☺ ☺ ☺ ☺

Date: __/__/__

Today,I am grateful for:

_____
_____
_____

How will I make today awesome?

_____
_____
_____

Positive affirmations:

_____
_____
_____

They can conquer who believe they can.

Virgil

today's amazing moments:

_____
_____
_____

How could I have made this day even better?

_____
_____
_____

Goals/Plans for Tomorrow:

I am feel

_____   ☺ ☺ ☺ ☺
_____

Date: __/__/__

Today, I am grateful for:
_____
_____
_____

How will I make today awesome?
_____
_____
_____

Positive affirmations:
_____
_____
_____

We make the world we live in and shape our own environment.

Orison Swett Marden

today's amazing moments:
_____
_____
_____

How could I have made this day even better?
_____
_____
_____

Goals/Plans for Tomorrow: *I am feel*
_____   ☺ ☺ ☺ ☺
_____

Date: __/__/__

Today, I am grateful for:

_____
_____

_____

How will I make today awesome?

_____
_____

_____

Positive affirmations:

_____
_____

_____

True happiness involves the full use of one's power and talents.

John W. Gardner

today's amazing moments:

_____
_____

_____

How could I have made this day even better?

_____
_____

_____

Goals/Plans for Tomorrow:

_____

_____

I am feel

☺ ☺ ☺ ☹

Date: ___/___/___

Today, I am grateful for:

_____
_____
_____

How will I make today awesome?

_____
_____
_____

Positive affirmations:

_____
_____
_____

Crave for a thing, you will get it. Renounce the craving, the object will follow you by itself.

Swami Sivananda

today's amazing moments:

_____
_____
_____

How could I have made this day even better?

_____
_____
_____

Goals/Plans for Tomorrow:

_____   *I am feel*

☺ ☺ ☺ ☺

Date: __/__/__

Today,I am grateful for:

_____
_____
_____

How will I make today awesome?

_____
_____
_____

Positive affirmations:

_____
_____
_____

*How do you know you're going to do something,
untill you do it?*

J. D. Salinger

today's amazing moments:

_____
_____
_____

How could I have made this day even better?

_____
_____
_____

Goals/Plans for Tomorrow:

I am feel

_____   ☺ ☺ ☺ ☺
_____

Date: __/__/__

Today, I am grateful for:

_____
_____
_____

How will I make today awesome?

_____
_____
_____

Positive affirmations:

_____
_____
_____

Press forward. Do not stop, do not linger in your journey, but strive for the mark set before you.

George Whitefield

today's amazing moments:

_____
_____
_____

How could I have made this day even better?

_____
_____
_____

Goals/Plans for Tomorrow:

_____   *I am feel*

_____   ☺ ☺ ☺ ☺

Date: __/__/__

Today, I am grateful for:
_____
_____
_____

How will I make today awesome?
_____
_____
_____

Positive affirmations:
_____
_____
_____

Motivation is the art of getting people to do what you want them to do because they want to do it.
                                   Dwight D. Eisenhower

today's amazing moments:
_____
_____
_____

How could I have made this day even better?
_____
_____
_____

Goals/Plans for Tomorrow:
                                   I am feel
_____
_____   ☺ ☺ ☺ ☺

Date: __/__/__

Today, I am grateful for:

_____
_____
_____

How will I make today awesome?

_____
_____
_____

Positive affirmations:

_____
_____
_____

Our greatest weakness lies in giving up. The most certain way to succeed is always to try just one more time.
                                        Thomas A. Edison

today's amazing moments:

_____
_____
_____

How could I have made this day even better?

_____
_____
_____

Goals/Plans for Tomorrow:

_____   *I am feel*

_____   ☺ ☺ ☺ ☺

Date: __/__/__

Today,I am grateful for:

_____
_____
_____

How will I make today awesome?

_____
_____
_____

Positive affirmations:

_____
_____
_____

Motivation is the art of getting people to do what you want them to do because they want to do it.
                                    Dwight D. Eisenhower

today's amazing moments:

_____
_____
_____

How could I have made this day even better?

_____
_____
_____

Goals/Plans for Tomorrow:

_____   I am feel

_____   ☺ ☺ ☺ ☺

Date: __/__/__

Today, I am grateful for:

_____
_____
_____

How will I make today awesome?

_____
_____
_____

Positive affirmations:

_____
_____
_____

Our greatest weakness lies in giving up. The most certain way to succeed is always to try just one more time.
                                        Thomas A. Edison

today's amazing moments:

_____
_____
_____

How could I have made this day even better?

_____
_____
_____

Goals/Plans for Tomorrow:

                                    I am feel
_____   ☺ ☺ ☺ ☺
_____

Date: __/__/__

Today, I am grateful for:

_____
_____

_____

How will I make today awesome?

_____
_____

_____

Positive affirmations:

_____
_____

_____

Our greatest weakness lies in giving up. The most certain way to succeed is always to try just one more time.
                                    Thomas A. Edison

today's amazing moments:

_____

_____

_____

How could I have made this day even better?

_____
_____

_____

Goals/Plans for Tomorrow:

_____   *I am feel*

_____   ☺ ☺ ☺ ☺

Date: __/__/__

Today, I am grateful for:

_____
_____
_____

How will I make today awesome?

_____
_____
_____

Positive affirmations:

_____
_____
_____

Our greatest weakness lies in giving up. The most certain way to succeed is always to try just one more time.
Thomas A. Edison

today's amazing moments:

_____
_____
_____

How could I have made this day even better?

_____
_____
_____

Goals/Plans for Tomorrow:

_____

I am feel

☺ ☺ ☺ ☺

Date: __/__/__

Today, I am grateful for:

_____
_____

_____

How will I make today awesome?

_____
_____

_____

Positive affirmations:

_____
_____

_____

Our greatest weakness lies in giving up. The most certain way to succeed is always to try just one more time.
                                        Thomas A. Edison

today's amazing moments:

_____
_____

_____

How could I have made this day even better?

_____
_____

_____

Goals/Plans for Tomorrow:

_____   *I am feel*

_____   ☺ ☺ ☺ ☺

Date: __/__/__

Today,I am grateful for:
_____
_____
_____

How will I make today awesome?
_____
_____
_____

Positive affirmations:
_____
_____
_____

Our greatest weakness lies in giving up· The most certain way to succeed is always to try just one more time·
Thomas A· Edison

today's amazing moments:
_____
_____
_____

How could I have made this day even better?
_____
_____
_____

Goals/Plans for Tomorrow:

I am feel

_____
☺ ☺ ☺ ☺
_____

Date: __/__/__

Today,I am grateful for:

_____
_____
_____

How will I make today awesome?

_____
_____
_____

Positive affirmations:

_____
_____
_____

Our greatest weakness lies in giving up. The most certain way to succeed is always to try just one more time.
Thomas A. Edison

today's amazing moments:

_____
_____
_____

How could I have made this day even better?

_____
_____
_____

Goals/Plans for Tomorrow:

_____   *I am feel*
_____   ☺ ☺ ☺ ☺

I am feel